MW00605132

WILDFLOWER FOLK
COLORING BOOK

Christine Karron

WILDFLOWER FOLK
COLORING BOOK

Published by Blue Angel Publishing®
80 Glen Tower Drive, Glen Waverley
Victoria, Australia 3150
info@blueangelonline.com
blueangelonline.com

By Christine Karron

Edited by Cherise Asmah

Blue Angel Publishing is a registered
trademark of Blue Angel Gallery Pty. Ltd.

ISBN: 978-1-922573-49-0

WILDFLOWER WELCOME

I'm incredibly excited to present this special coloring book featuring my favorite and most popular illustrations. It wasn't easy deciding which images to include, as I have so many to choose from, and I love them all. I created four new artworks especially for this collection: *Daughter of the Sun*, *Sunkissed*, *Swallows*, and *Wildflower Ring*. I know you will enjoy meeting these wildflower folk as much as I did.

Drawing and creating art have always been a big part of my life. Many in my family are artistically gifted, so making art has always felt natural to me. My parents supported my creative expression from the start — I attended art school as a child and later a school for art and design, where I received my education in foundational academic arts. During these years, I learned that realism simply wasn't enough for me. As a dreamer with a big imagination, I wanted my illustrations to tell stories, so I started to combine whimsical touches and fantasy with a realistic approach.

Growing up, fairy tales and northern European folklore fascinated me and shaped my imagination. When reading children's books, I was always taken by the skillfully drawn illustrations and tried to learn from them. When playing and picking flowers and berries in forests so deep (just like the fairy tales), it felt as though there was a world beyond ours full of characters and stories to tell. These precious memories are the primary source of my fantasy illustrations today.

I hope this book brings you joy and many happy hours of relaxing coloring.

Christine Karron

AMBER

ANGEL EYES

BABY DRAGON

CRYSTAL

DANCING QUEENS

DARK EYES

DAUGHTER OF THE SUN

DEAR DIARY

DREAMY FAE

ENCHANTRESS

FAE DARLING

FAYE

FIRST SNOW

FLORA

FOREST SPRITE

FREE SPIRIT

GRANDMOTHER WITH HER GRANDDAUGHTER

HALLOWEEN TEA PARTY

KITTY CUDDLES

LADY WITCH

LAST HARVEST

LILIES AND PEARLS

LITTLE MERMAID

LITTLE RED RIDING HOOD

MELODY

MERMAID'S PEARL

MOTHER'S LOVE

NEOMA

OCEAN EYES

OLD WISE FAIRY

PEARLA

PEARLS OF LIFE

QUEEN OF THE SEVEN SEAS

QUEEN'S CHALICE

SACRED FEATHERS

SMALL WONDERS

SPRING AWAKENING

SPRING WIND

STEAMPUNK

SUGAR PLUM FAIRY

SUNKISSED

SWALLOWS

THISTLE LANDING

TIDES OF TIME

TROLL GIRL

WATER NYMPH

WHILE SUNFLOWERS BLOOM

WILDBERRY BLOOM

WILDFLOWER RING

WIND WHISPERS

WIZARD

WOOD ELFLING

WOODLAND HEALER

For more information on this or
any Blue Angel Publishing® release,
please visit our website at:

www.blueangelonline.com